Welcome to the castle of giant Dawub.
You must enter the castle and find the chest of gold.

1 Each letter of the giant's name has a line of symmetry.
Draw each line. Check with a mirror.

2 Draw the missing half of each letter to find
the name of Dawub's pet dragon.
Check with a mirror.

3 Complete the missing half to see Dawub's face.

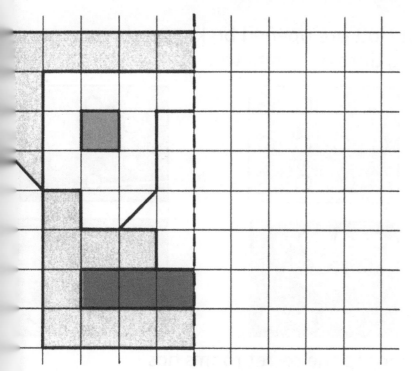

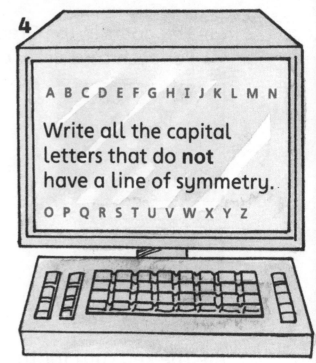

4 Write all the capital letters that do **not** have a line of symmetry.

A B C D E F G H I J K L M N
O P Q R S T U V W X Y Z

The Great Hall

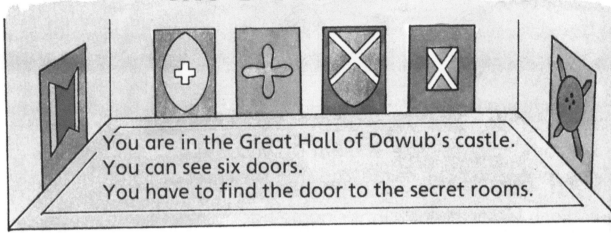

You are in the Great Hall of Dawub's castle.
You can see six doors.
You have to find the door to the secret rooms.

1 **(a)** Draw the line or lines of symmetry on each door.

(b) The secret door has only one line of symmetry.
Tick the secret door.

2 **(a)** The doors in the Great Hall are opened by key cards.
For each card draw any lines of symmetry.

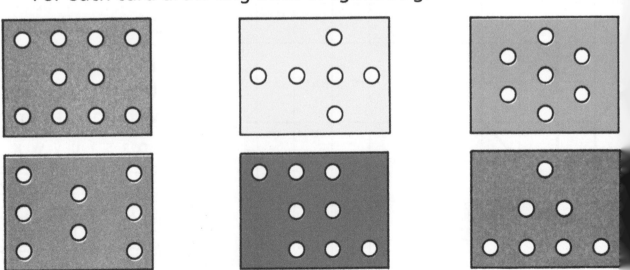

(b) The key card for the door to the secret rooms has
no lines of symmetry. Tick this card.

HEINEMANN MATHEMATICS 4

Name

SHAPE AND HANDLING DATA
WORKBOOK

Revised

Nature Trail

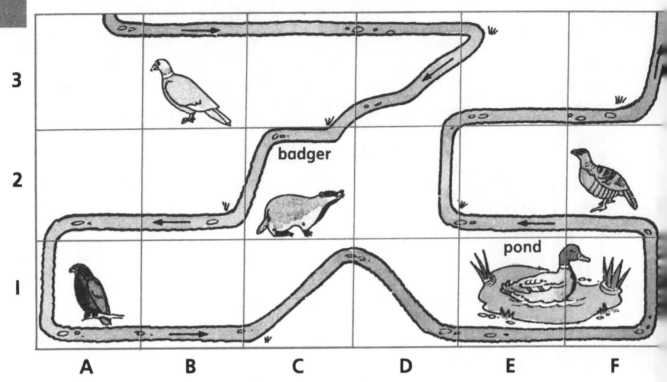

1 (a) Write these names on the map of the Nature Trail:

Pigeon at **B3**   Grouse at **F2**   Hawk at **A1**

(b) Draw a pine tree at **E3** and a toadstool at **A2**.

(c) Draw and name on the map three other things found on nature trails. Complete:

Name	Position

Name	Position

Name	Position

2 (a) Colour the **shortest** tunnel to the badger's set.

(b) Write each position this tunnel passes through. Start at **T6**.

T6

(c) Do this again for the **longest** tunnel.

T6

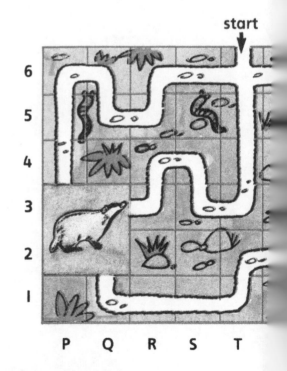

Ask your teacher what to do next.

You enter the first secret room.
You have to find a pathway to the chest of gold.

I **(a)** Colour the floors of the four rooms so that each room
has two lines of symmetry.

(b) To find the treasure, you can only walk on red squares.
Draw a pathway to the treasure.

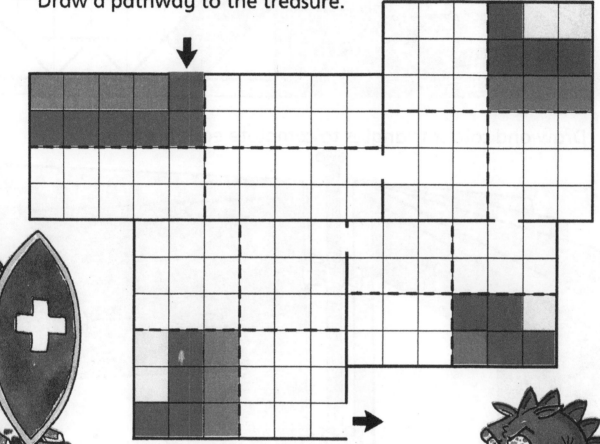

Well done. You have found the treasure chest.

2 To open the chest, colour the squares so that
each design has the lines of symmetry shown.

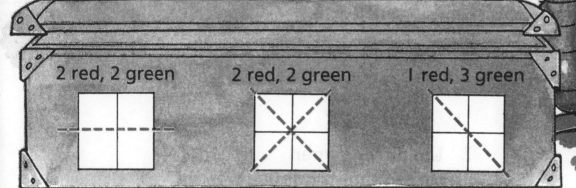

2 red, 2 green   2 red, 2 green   I red, 3 green

Ask your teacher what to do next.

H 61

Carpet bazaar

1 Draw and colour squares to complete the wall tiling.

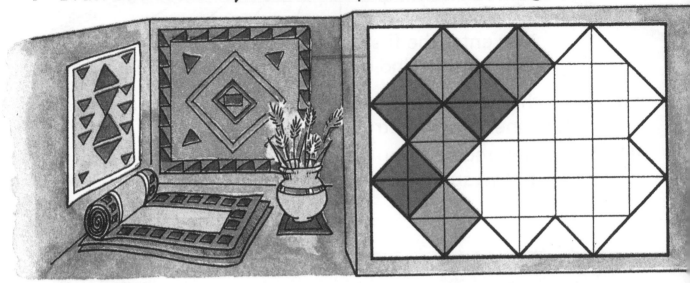

2 Draw and colour triangles to complete each pattern.

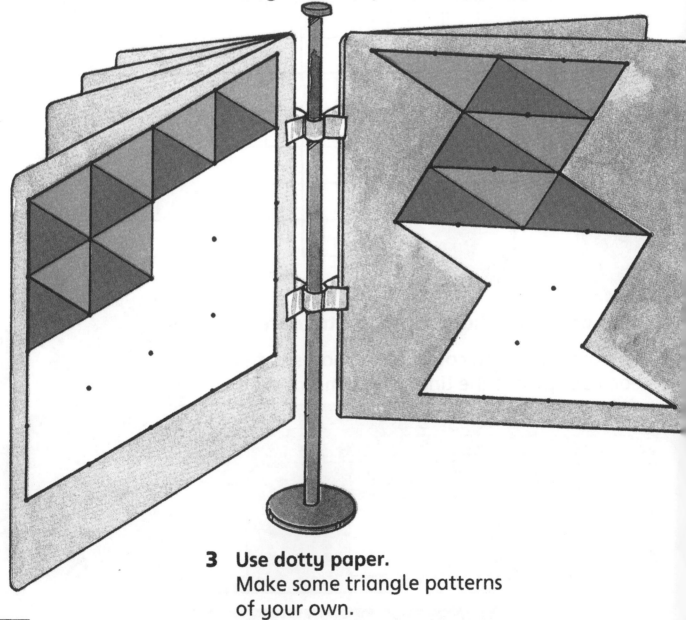

3 Use dotty paper.
Make some triangle patterns
of your own.

I Complete the patterns.

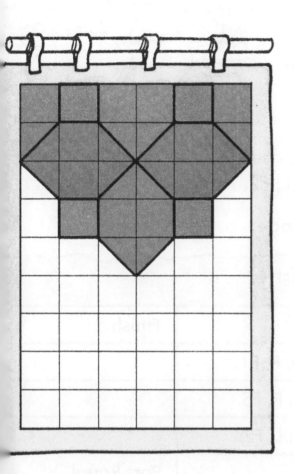

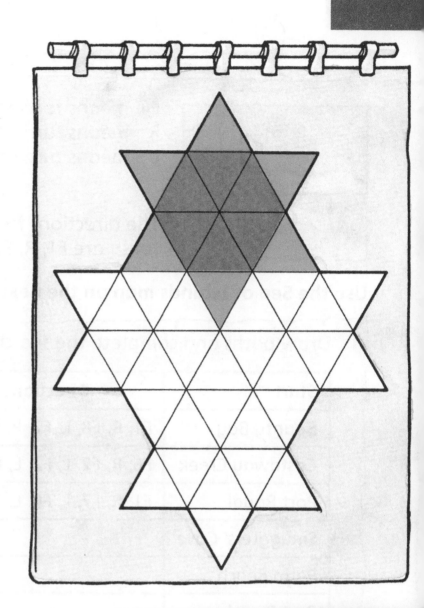

2 **Use squared paper.**
Draw and colour some patterns of your own.

Ask your teacher what to do next.

H62

Ship ahoy!

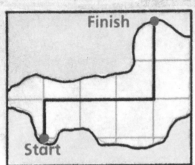

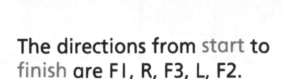

F4 means forward 4.
R means turn right.
L means turn left.

The directions from start to
finish are F1, R, F3, L, F2.

Use the Sea of Islands map on the next page.

1 Draw paths and complete the sea chart.

Start	Directions	Finish
Bounty Bay	F1, R, F8, L, F2, R, F4, R, F1.	
Castaway Creek	F6, R, F2, L, F2, L, F2, R, F5.	
Port Royal	F1, R, F7, L, F6, L, F3, L, F2.	
Smugglers' Cove		Port Royal
Palm Beach		Castaway Creek
Port Royal		Bounty Bay

2 All ye who seek the sunken loot,
Use these directions to plan your route.

Start at Port Royal.

F1, L, F9, R, F13, R, F6, L, F3, R, F4, R, F2, R, F1.

Mark the position with a cross.

3 Draw a shorter path to the treasure.
Write the directions for your path.

4 Draw your own map on squared paper.
Write directions for a friend to follow.

Sea of Islands

Port Royal

Little Island

Castaway Creek

Smugglers' Cove

Wreck Reef

Bounty Bay

Palm Beach

Open the treasure chest

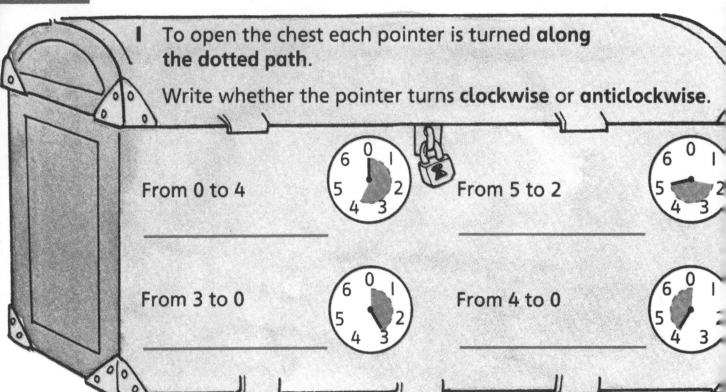

I To open the chest each pointer is turned **along the dotted path.**

Write whether the pointer turns **clockwise** or **anticlockwise.**

From 0 to 4 _____

From 5 to 2 _____

From 3 to 0 _____

From 4 to 0 _____

2 Complete the table for Captain Bill's turns in his cabin.

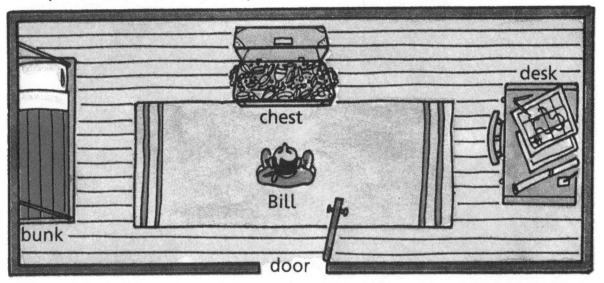

Bill faces	he turns	he now faces
chest	I quarter turn clockwise	
bunk	I quarter turn anticlockwise	
door	I half turn clockwise	
desk	I half turn anticlockwise	

Extension

door		desk

Ben, the lighthouse keeper

1 Complete the table for the lamp switch.

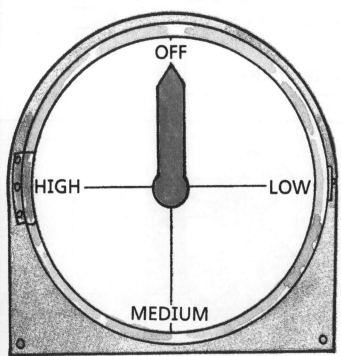

Start at	Turn	Finish at
OFF	1 right angle clockwise	
LOW	2 right angles clockwise	
MEDIUM	1 right angle anticlockwise	
HIGH	2 right angles anticlockwise	
LOW	3 right angles clockwise	
HIGH	4 right angles anticlockwise	

2 Complete the table for Ben, the lighthouse keeper.

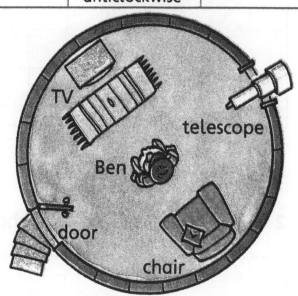

Ben faces	he turns through	he now faces
T.V.	1 right angle anticlockwise	
telescope	3 right angles clockwise	
chair	2 right angles clockwise	
door	3 right angles anticlockwise	
telescope	4 right angles clockwise	
chair		telescope

Extension

Shape puzzles

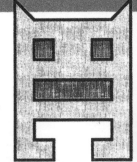

I **(a)** Draw and colour the missing half of each symmetrical mask.

(b) Find the area of each completed mask.

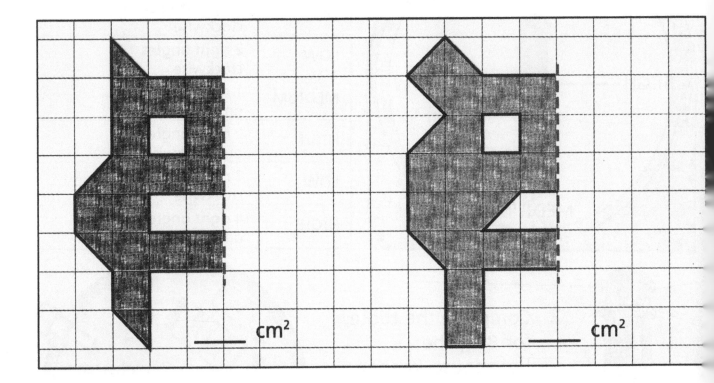

_____ cm²

_____ cm²

Problem solving

2 (a) Find the area of each shape.

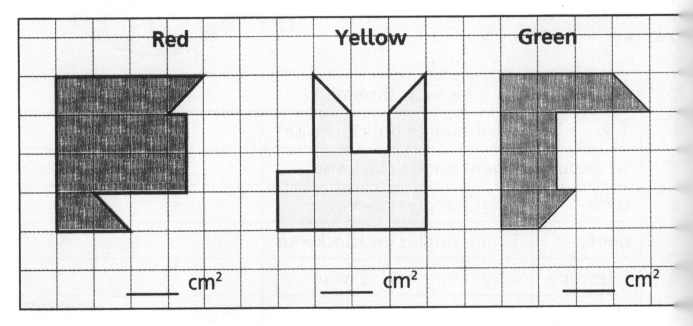

Red   Yellow   Green

_____ cm²   _____ cm²   _____ cm²

(b) Which two shapes join together to make a rectangle?

_____ and _____

Fabrics

I Colour the rug to make it symmetrical.

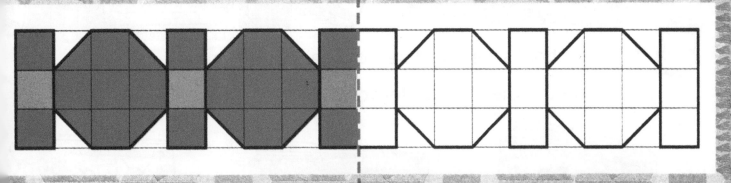

2 Draw and colour the missing half of each symmetrical design.

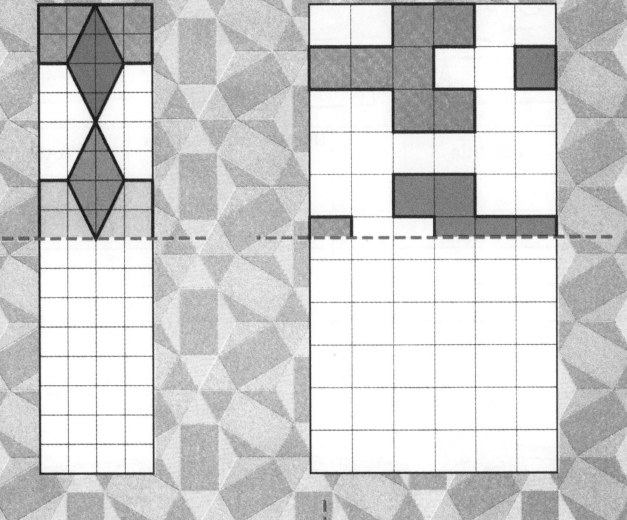

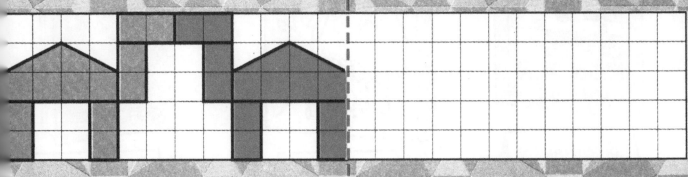

Readathon

I These books were ordered at the readathon.

Complete the book order form.

42 copies

15 copies

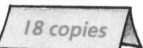
18 copies

Book title	Number of books	Cost per book	Total
			£
			£
			£
			£
			£
			£
		Total cost	£

6 copies

10 copies

19 copies

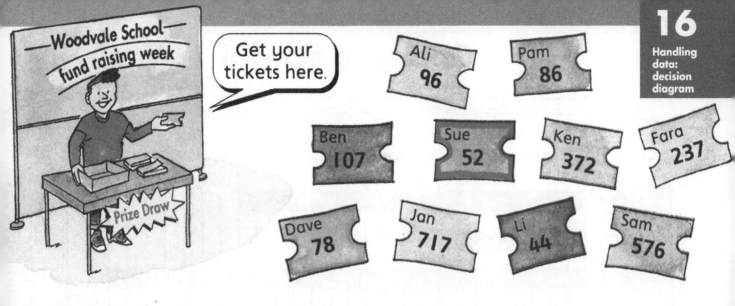

1 Ten children wrote their names on their tickets.
   Take each ticket through the tree diagram.

   Write the children's names
   in the boxes.

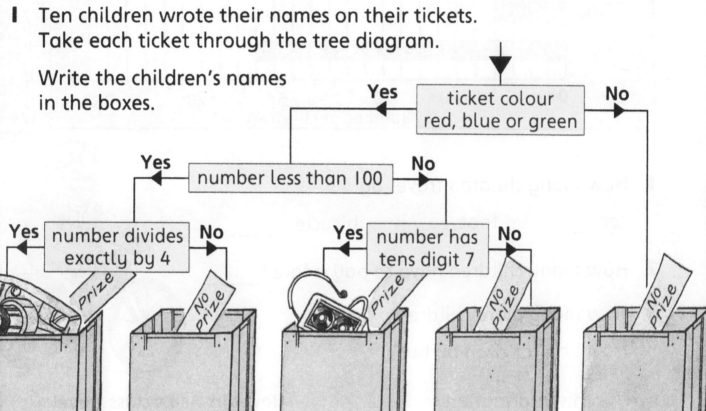

2 Is it possible to win a camera **and** a personal stereo
   with one ticket? Explain your answer.

   _____

   _____

Extension

3 Colour and number a different winning ticket for

   a camera   a personal stereo

Ask your teacher what to do next.

Going to school

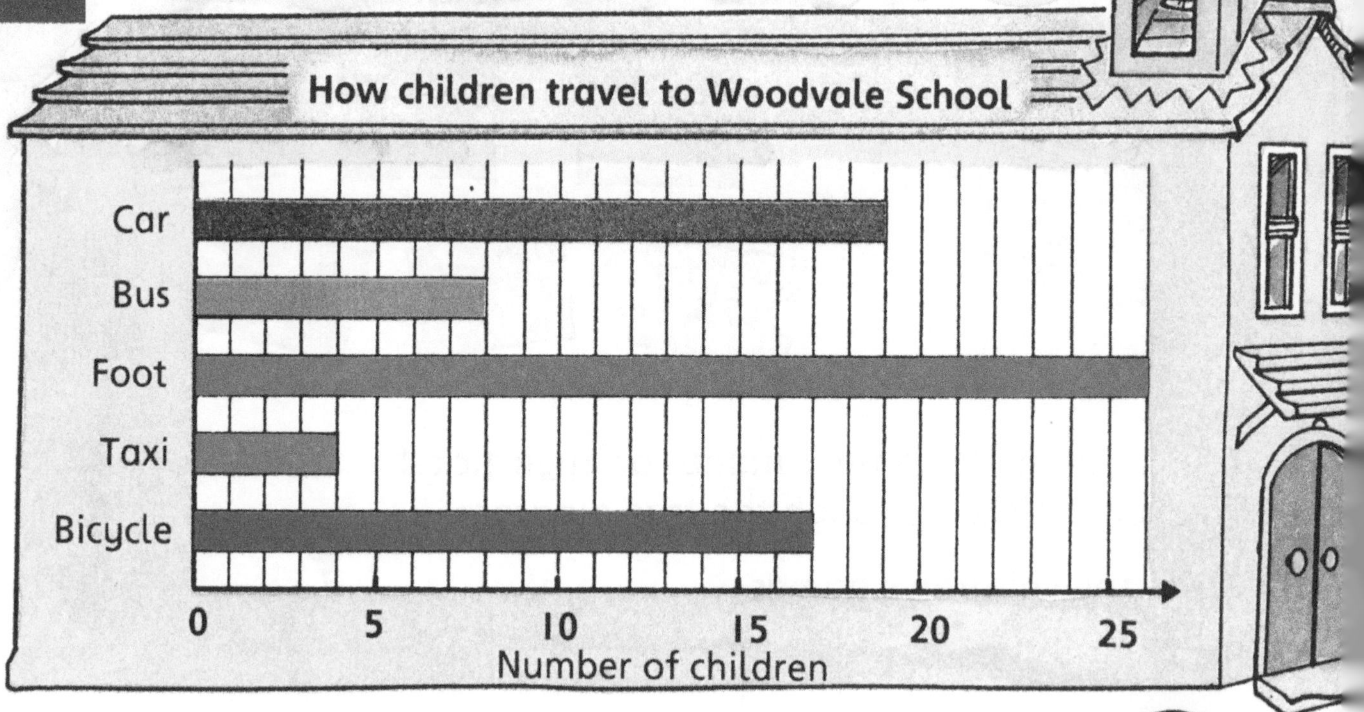
How children travel to Woodvale School
Car
Bus
Foot
Taxi
Bicycle
0
5
10
15
20
25
Number of children

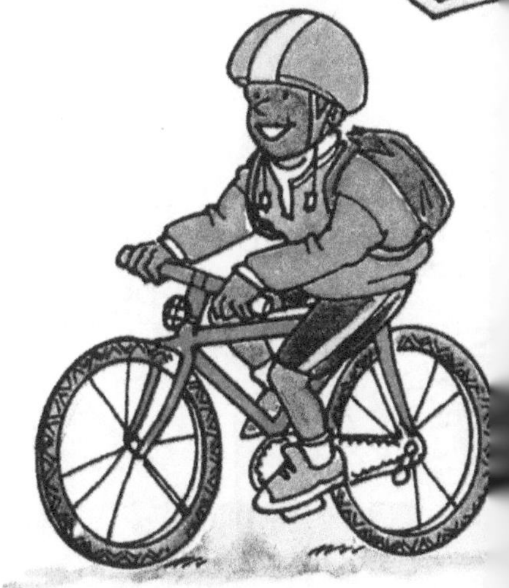

1 How many children travel by

car _____ foot _____ bicycle _____

2 How many children have to pay a fare? _____

3 How many more children travel by car than by bus? _____

4 Use this information to draw a graph.

Mrs Asif's class	
Form of transport	**Number of children**
Car	6
Bus	3
Foot	9
Taxi	1
Bicycle	2

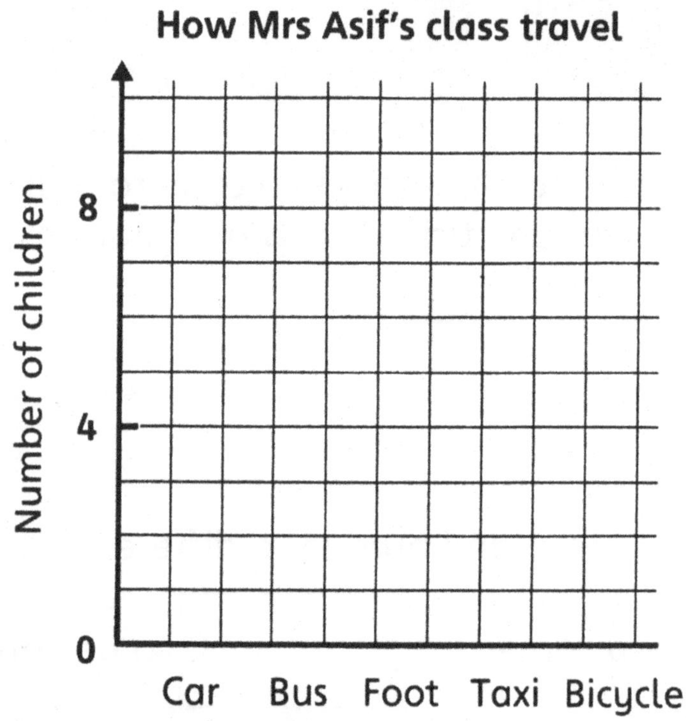
How Mrs Asif's class travel
Number of children
8
4
0
Car
Bus
Foot
Taxi
Bicycle

Go to Textbook page 89.

Collections

1 Complete to show the number of coins.

⬭ represents 10 coins

	Between						
Alvin	20 and 30	⬭	⬭	⬭	⬭	⬭	⬭
Lucy	10 and 20	⬭	⬭	⬭	⬭	⬭	⬭
Aziz	40 and 50	⬭	⬭	⬭	⬭	⬭	⬭
Amy	30 and 40	⬭	⬭	⬭	⬭	⬭	⬭
Cara	50 and 60	⬭	⬭	⬭	⬭	⬭	⬭
Sam	0 and 10	⬭	⬭	⬭	⬭	⬭	⬭

2 Complete to show the number of stamps.

■ represents 100 stamps

	Between						
Elaine	100 and 200	☐	☐	☐	☐	☐	☐
Joel	500 and 600	☐	☐	☐	☐	☐	☐
Shamina	0 and 100	☐	☐	☐	☐	☐	☐
Marcus	400 and 500	☐	☐	☐	☐	☐	☐
Vicky	600 and 700	☐	☐	☐	☐	☐	☐
Clyde	300 and 400	☐	☐	☐	☐	☐	☐
Emma	200 and 300	☐	☐	☐	☐	☐	☐

Ask your teacher what to do next.

Superstars

Work with a group.

1 Complete your **Superstar File** on page 20 and cut it out.

2 Use 8 of the Superstar files.

Write names to complete each Carroll diagram.

	cycle	~~cycle~~
play chess		
~~play chess~~		

	swim	~~swim~~
whistle		
~~whistle~~		

3 Use **all** of the Superstar files.

Tick (✔) to show how many people can do these.

		Total
cycle		
skip		
whistle		
play a keyboard		
swim		
spread fingers		
play chess		

4 Use the table on page 19, question 3.
Choose **4** things that people can do.

Draw a graph.

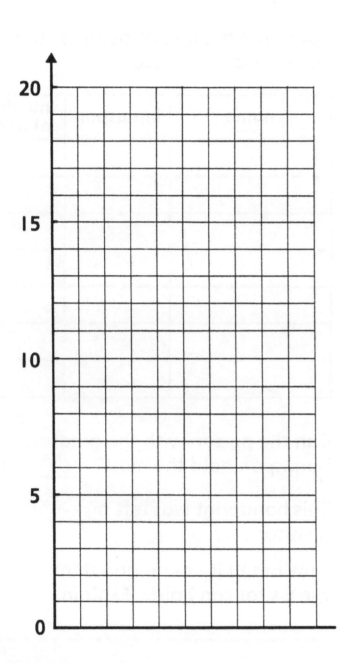

5 Use **all** of the Superstar files.
Who are the Superstars in your class?

_____

_____

_____

Superstar File

name _____

Tick

	yes	no
	yes	no
	yes	no
	yes	no
	yes	no
	yes	no
	yes	no
	yes	no

Handspans

Work as a group.

1   Measure and record each person's handspan.

2   Count the number of beads or marbles each person can hold.

name	handspan	number of items

3   Can the person with the greatest handspan hold the most? _____

4   This handprint was left by a visitor.

How many items do you think the visitor can hold? Explain.

_____

_____

_____

_____

_____

_____

The memory test

Ask your teacher how to play the memory test.

objects	names				total
total					

1 Write the total for • each person • each object
in the table.

2 Which objects were
remembered by everyone? _____

3 Which object did most people forget? _____

4 Who remembered the largest number of objects? _____

5 Who remembered the
same number of objects? _____

6 Who remembered **more
than half** the objects? _____

Ask your teacher what to do next.

Shape and Handling Data: Record of Work

Name _____   Class _____

Shape and Handling Data Workbook / Textbook / Reinforcement Sheets / Check-ups

Shape

3D Shape

T76	T77	T78	T79	T80	Check-up 1

Grid references

T82	W1	Check-up 2

Symmetry

W2	T83	T84	W3	W4	Check-up 2

Tiling

W5	W6	Check-up 2

Right angles

W7	W8	W9	W10	T85	T86	Check-up 3

Other activities

T81	W11	W14

Handling Data

Handling data

T87	T88	W15	W16	W17	T89	T90	W18	Check-up 1	Check-up 2

Survey

W19	W20	W21	W22	Check-up 3

Other activities

T91	T92	T93

Heinemann is an imprint of Pearson Education Limited, a company incorporated in England and Wales, having its registered office at Edinburgh Gate, Harlow, Essex, CM20 2JE. Registered company number: 872828
ISBN 978 0 435 03103 9 © Scottish Primary Mathematics Group 1992/5.
First published 1992. Revised edition 1995.   19   30
Produced by Oxprint Ltd, Oxford. Illustrated by Oxford Illustrators.
Printed and bound in Great Britain by Ashford Colour Press Ltd

ISBN 978-0-435031-03-9

9 780435 031039